# JAMES MORRISON
## UNDISCOVERED

**WISE PUBLICATIONS**
part of The Music Sales Group
London / New York / Paris / Sydney / Copenhagen / Berlin / Madrid / Tokyo

Published by
Wise Publications
14-15 Berners Street, London, W1T 3LJ, UK.

Exclusive distributors:
Music Sales Limited
Distribution Centre, Newmarket Road,
Bury St Edmunds, Suffolk, IP33 3YB, UK.

Music Sales Pty Limited
120 Rothschild Avenue, Rosebery,
NSW 2018, Australia.

Order No. AM986645
ISBN 1-84609-678-2
This book © Copyright 2006 Wise Publications,
a division of Music Sales Limited.

Edited by Chris Harvey.
Music arranged by Derek Jones.
Music processed by Paul Ewers Music Design.

Printed in the EU.

www.musicsales.com

# Under The Influence

Words & Music by James Morrison, Steve McEwan & Jimmy Hogarth

*Vocal/Instrumental ad lib.*

1. I was

Well, just when I thought I had it planned out.
Oh, but some-how mak-ing me come clean now. What-
-ev-er I do I'm un-der the in-flu-ence of you.

What-ev-er I do I'm un-der the in-flu-ence of
you.

Once you've had a taste_ of it there's no go-ing back._

Once you've had a taste_ of it there's

*1.*

no go-ing back._

*2.*

no go-ing back._

*D.S. al Coda*

What -

*Drums*

⊕ *Coda*

*1.*

*2.*

# You Give Me Something

Words & Music by James Morrison & Eg White

1. You on - ly stay___ with me___ in the morn - ing,_____
2. You on - ly wait - ed up___ for hours,_____

you on - ly hold___ me when___ I sleep.___
just to spend a lit - tle time a - lone with me.___

# Wonderful World

### Words & Music by James Morrison & Eg White

# The Pieces Don't Fit Anymore

Words & Music by James Morrison, Martin Brammer & Steve Robson

closing me in,_____ closing the space_ in my heart.
hide all the bruis-es, I hide all the da - mage that's done.

But I

Watch-ing us fad-ing and watch-ing it all fall a - part.
show how I'm feel-ing un - til all the feel-ing has gone.

Well, I

can't ex-plain_____ why it's not e-nough 'cause I gave it all_____ to you.

And if you

leave me now,_____ oh, just leave me now,_____ it's the bet-ter thing_____ to do.

It's

*To Coda* ⊕

# One Last Chance

*Words & Music by James Morrison, Tim Kellett & Kevin Andrews*

Once_____ I had e - ve - ry - thing, now it's gone.___
Don't say_____ that you__ have giv - en

up on____ me.
Don't tell me a - gain___ 'cause I've heard it all__ be - fore.___
Just give me the time__ and space to__ heal my__ head.___

Some peo - ple say that I'm__ not worth__ it.

I've made mis - takes but no - bo - dy's per - fect.

Guess I'll give it a try._____ I've got

one last chance to get my-self to-geth-er._____ I
can lose no more time, it's now or nev-er._____ And I try_
_____ to re-mem-ber who I_____ used_ to_ be._____ I've got
one last chance to get my-self to-geth-er._____ - er._____ And I_

# Undiscovered

Words & Music by James Morrison, Martin Brammer & Steve Robson

1. I look at you,_ you bite_ your tongue, you don't_
(2.) time it takes_ to know_ some - one,_ it all_

_ know why_ or where_ I'm com - ing from._____ But
_ can change be - fore_ you know it's gone._____ So

in my head__ I'm close__ to you,__ we're in____ the rain__ still search - ing for__ the
close your eyes__ and feel__ the way__ I'm with__ you now,__ be - lieve__ there's no - thing

sun.____
wrong.__

You think that I__ wan-na run__ and

hide.__ I keep it all__ locked up__ in - side.__ I just want__ you to find__ me.__ I'm not

lost. I'm not__ lost,__ just un - dis - cov - ered.__ And when we're a - lone__

we're all the same\_ as\_ each oth - er.\_\_\_\_ You

see the look\_ that's on\_ my face,\_\_\_\_ you might think\_ that I'm out\_

\_ of place.\_\_\_\_ I'm not\_ lost,\_\_\_\_ no, no,\_ just un - dis - cov -

**1.**

**To Coda**

\- ered.\_\_\_\_ 2. Well, the \_\_\_\_ no, no,\_ just un - dis - cov -

**2.**

35

36

# The Letter

Words & Music by  James Morrison, David Frank & Wayne Hector

Lyrics:

1. It's got my name on it  and it's just wait-ing there for me.
2. There must be a name for it,  what-ev-er this is you've done to me.

get her._____ She was no good___ for me. Deep down___ I know that's the way it has to be, so

how come I still can't op-en this let-ter?_____ I can't___ for -

-get her.

Real-ly wish I could.

- get her._____ Oh,_____ I real-ly wish I

41

# Call The Police

Words & Music by James Morrison & Eg White

I write it down and tell you ex-act-ly how I feel a-gain. And all I see_____ is a

mass of con-fu-sion, who I am and what I got-ta be._____

2. Closed eyes, big__ lines.__ I get so tempt-ed just to let it ride some-times.
3. I'm a-wake, why wait?__ I don't need some-one to tell me who to be to-day.

Looks good, tastes bad,__ it makes me won-der where I bur-ied all the dreams I had.
I'm quite sure, like be-fore, came off the road and I for-got what I was look-ing for.

44

# This Boy

Words & Music by  James Morrison & Tim Kellett

1. This boy wants to play,___ there's no time___ left to - day.___ It's a shame___ 'cause he has_
2. This girl tries her best___ ev - 'ry day___ but it's all___ gone to waste___ 'cause there's no-

I'm still here_____ but it has-n't been ea - sy.

I'm sure_____ that you had your rea - sons. I'm scared_____ of

**1.**
all this e - mo - tion. For years I've been hold - ing it down._____ For

**2.**
years I've been hold - ing it down._____ years I've been hold - ing it down.__

give and for-get___ so I'll___ try to put all this be-hind___ us. Just

know___ that my arms are wide op - en. The old - er I get___ the more___

___ that I know._____ Well,___ it's time to let___ this go.___

# If The Rain Must Fall

### Words & Music by James Morrison & Martin Terefe

Original key B major.

♩. = 60

1. Oh, life can be strange._ Good and
(2.) dreams can come true_ if you know in-

bad_ in so ma-ny ways. And in time you will find that
-side you real-ly want them to. You can sit, you can wait, you can

things aren't al-ways what they seem._ No._ Well, I've
leave your fate in some-one else's_ hands. Oh, but

is your love. That's all I need. All I need is

**1.** your love. 2. Oh, well, Your love. *Vocal ad lib.*

57

# How Come

*Words & Music by James Morrison, Jimmy Hogarth & Steve McEwan*

See, I got to know_ be-fore it's ov-er,_____ one way or the oth-er, if you're

string-ing me a - long._____

*D.S. al Coda*

How come?_____ How come?_____

How come you al-ways wind up chang-ing your di - rec-tion?

# The Last Goodbye

Words & Music by James Morrison, Jimmy Hogarth & Steve McEwan

1, (3.) And I don't be - lieve___ you___ and I nev - er will.___
(2.)___ you___ but may - be I nev - er did___

walk-ing a-way____ from you____ and I'm not com-ing__back.    3. I don't be - lieve

Vocal ad lib.

# Better Man

Words & Music by James Morrison, Julian Gallagher & Kim Richie

123456789